Nelson

Copyright © 2011 by
Rob Davis, Woodrow Phoenix
and Blank Slate Books

First published 2011 by
Blank Slate Books, London

Nelson Editors:
Rob Davis and Woodrow Phoenix
Book Co-ordinator:
Kayla Marie Hillier
Publisher:
Kenny Penman
Group Editor:
Iz Rips
Publicity and Marketing:
Martin Steenton

Publication Design:
SuperAdaptoid at Detonator

ISBN: 978–1–906653–23–1

Printed in Poland

Discover more about Blank Slate at
www.blankslatebooks.co.uk

All the profits from the first 4,000
copies of 'Nelson' sold will go to
Shelter, the housing and home-
lessness charity. With Blank Slate
Books' support, Shelter can help
more people find and keep a home
in a place where they can thrive.
Retailers are also being asked to
donate a share of their sales profits
to Shelter, Charity Number 263710
(England & Wales); SC002327
(Scotland).

son

Blank Slate Books

Nel

edited by **Rob Davis**
and **Woodrow Phoenix**

Blank Slate Books

Nel-son

Afterword

THERE IS an invisible jigsaw in this book that you could put together if you knew where to look for the pieces. A secret history, a kind of group auto-biography, comprised of memories and reflections from each of the creators of Nelson. In trying to accurately recreate the texture of bygone years, we spent a long time discussing the details: toys, fads, food obsessions, fashions, politics, stupid films, family holidays on strict budgets in basic seaside chalets and under wet canvas, brothers and sisters (and their weird girlfriends and meathead boyfriends). How did you survive your first day at school? When did Space Hoppers appear? How do you make a Knickerbocker Glory? What time was it when Neil Armstrong stepped onto the moon? Did you support Blur or Oasis in the Britpop wars? How much did a roll of that heat-sensitive fax machine paper cost in 1990? What does it feel like to take Prozac? Who was the first person you called with your mobile phone? Where were you when Kurt Cobain/Princess Diana/Michael Jackson died? Have you ever punched someone? Which one of your parents are you most like? Have you ever gone on a protest march? Do you think voting changes anything? Do you buy lottery tickets? Do you have children? Why is it strange not to want them?

We compared our answers, then buried them deep in our stories to underpin the details we invented for Nel Baker's life. I gave Nel a twin brother and then took him away because my mother lost her twin the same way. And because my sister died decades ago, but I still think about what our lives would be like if she had lived. Just as I drew those things from my experiences, many of us took little pieces of ourselves and reshaped them into little pieces of this book. Everyone added their own story thread, some crucial, some incidental, some will take second and third reads to discover, all of them woven into the whole. We are all Nelson and Nelson is a composite of all of us.

Rob and I started this project with no idea where it was going to go. From the beginning, it ran away from us in directions that we hadn't anticipated. Every time we were sure about what was going to happen next, we were wrong. But we were happy to be wrong. That was how we knew that it was taking on a life of its own. It was a wild and sometimes uncomfortable ride, but mostly it has been exhilarating proof of what the comics medium can do: taking blank paper, pencil and ink, and transmuting them into imagination, emotion and beauty.

WOODROW PHOENIX

Biographies

Biographies

PAUL GRIST
1967

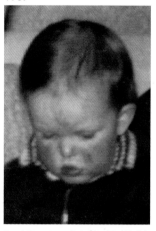

Paul Grist was born in Sheffield and now lives near Bristol. His first comics were published in the 1980s by DC Thomson and Fleetway. He went on to collaborate with Grant Morrison on the celebrated *St. Swithin's Day*. Paul has written and drawn *Spider-Man, Batman* and *Superman* stories for Marvel and DC, and more recently has drawn for the Doctor Who spin-off series *Torchwood*.

Paul began his own publishing company in the 1990s, Dancing Elephant Press, publishing *Burglar Bill*, the critically acclaimed crime drama *Kane*, and the superhero saga *Jack Staff*, before moving them to Image Comics in 2002. There are six book collections of *Kane* and four collections of *Jack Staff* available.

Paul is currently working on a new book, *Mudman*, to be published by Image in 2011.
www.bigcosmiccomic.blogspot.com
www.twitter.com/mistergrist

ROB DAVIS
1968

Rob Davis was born in deepest, darkest, Dorset into an age when comics were as commonplace as cigarettes and sideburns.

He produced the odd-ball psychedelic comic, *SLANG*, from 1989 to 1991 with Sean Longcroft, and from there began working professionally on mainstays of the British comics landscape *Roy of the Rovers* and *Judge Dredd*. Disillusioned that the world of comics didn't match what he'd hoped to find, he separated the words and pictures, earning a living as an illustrator, and writing for himself. During this time he drew for the *Guardian*, BBC magazines, Scholastic Books and Random House, among others.

In 2005, Rob returned to comics work, writing and later drawing the comic strip for *Doctor Who Magazine*, producing webcomics, and shorts for *Solipsistic Pop*. He has plans for many more comics in the future. Rob is currently adapting and drawing *Don Quixote* for SelfMadeHero.
www.dinlosandskilldos.blogspot.com

WOODROW PHOENIX
1969

Woodrow Phoenix grew up with four sisters in Brockley, South London. He has been creating comics, animation, design and illustration for editorial, advertising and publishing since 1988, including: weekly strips, *The Sumo Family*, (The *Independent on Sunday), Donny Digits*, (the *Guardian*), and a quarterly strip, *The Liberty Cat*, (*Comics Morning*, Kodansha, Japan). Woodrow has illustrated several children's books, and recently, written and drawn *That's a Horse of a Different Colour* and *Donny Digits* for *The DFC*.

With his frequent collaborator, Ian Carney, he created *SugarBuzz!*, an anthology comic featuring Pants Ant and Where's it at, Sugar Kat? that were optioned for television by Walt Disney, The Cartoon Network and other companies. He is the author of the book *Plastic Culture: How Japanese Toys Conquered the World*, published by Kodansha International, and *Rumble Strip*, published by Myriad Editions.
www.woodrowphoenix.co.uk

ELLEN LINDNER
1970

Born in the New York City suburbs, Ellen Lindner has spent the last seven years drinking tea and drawing comics in South London. She published her first graphic novel as writer and illustrator in 2009, and plays a supporting role in both the Fleece Station art studio and the Whores of Mensa ladies' comics circle.
Ellen is the artist of *Little Rock Nine*, written by Marshall Poe and published by Simon & Schuster, and is also the author of *Undertow*, published in a revised edition by Soaring Penguin Press.
www.littlewhitebird.com

JAMIE SMART
1971

Jamie Smart draws comics for children, alternative sweary comics, and webcomics. In his spare time he likes to draw even more. Currently he writes and illustrates *Desperate Dan* for *The Dandy*. Jamie is the creator of *Space Raoul*, *Bear*, and *Ubu Bubu*, all published by SLG, *the* webcomics *Whubble* and *Khochi Wanaba*, and he is now engaged in the epic websaga *Corporate Skull*. His children's books *Find Chaffy* and *Find Chaffy Now* are published by Scholastic Books.
www.fumboo.com

GARY NORTHFIELD
1972

Gary Northfield was born in Romford and lives in Brockley, South London. Graduating with a degree in Illustration in 1992, Gary made his first minicomics *Bad Dog* and *Stupidmonsters* in 1999. He became an in-house illustrator at Eaglemoss Publications in 2002, working on projects such as *Horrible Histories* and *The Magical World Of Roald Dahl*. In 2004, his creator-owned strip *Derek The Sheep* began appearing in *the Beano*. A book collection of *Derek* followed four years later in the UK and France. Gary has drawn comic strips for publications including: *The Dandy*, *National Geographic Kids* and *The DFC*. His next book is published by Walker Books in 2012.
www.garynorthfield.co.uk

SARAH MCINTYRE
1973

Sarah McIntyre was born in Seattle, USA and lives in New Cross, London. She works with Gary Northfield, Ellen Lindner and Lauren O'Farrell in the Fleece Station, a studio in an old police station in South London, complete

with cells for clients who don't pay. One cell even has a ghost! She is the creator of *Vern and Lettuce*, a strip featuring a sheep and a rabbit which appeared weekly in *The DFC* before being published in a collection by David Fickling Books. Sarah has illustrated several picture books, including: *Morris the Mankiest Monster* by Giles Andreae, published by Picture Corgi; *You Can't Eat a Princess!* by Gillian Rogerson, published by Scholastic; and *When Titus Took the Train* by Anne Cottringer, published by Oxford University Press.
www.jabberworks.livejournal.com
www.jabberworks.co.uk

SUZY VARTY
1974

Suzy Varty lives in Newcastle. She has been fascinated by comics since she was a child. Her first comic was published in 1976 and she edited the first British women's comic anthology in 1977. Since then she's been published and exhibited in the USA, Europe and Scandinavia and worked with the medium in a variety of ways. She organized a comic art festival in Newcastle for Visual Arts Year 1996, produced a comic on a billboard, completed many artist's residencies, commissions and run comics courses.

She has produced several issue-based comics for publishers, and continues to champion this exciting yet underappreciated medium. Her work includes: BBC publications' *RaW* series; *Genetic Politics* for New Clarion Press; a comic for AWA Peace Organisation's book, published in Holland; *Women out of Line,* an anthology for Fanny Comics/Knockabout; *Wimmins Comix* for Last Gasp, *Partylines* for Thames TV publications; *The Comic Book of First Love* and *The Facts of Life* for Virago/Penguin; *Pork Roasts*; and *Mamadramas* for Kitchen Sink Comics.

SEAN LONGCROFT
1975

Sean Longcroft has two children, lives in Sussex, and has a lazy eye. At the very least. He likes blackberries, rust and hymenoptera. After his debut in the psychedelic comic, *SLANG*, he went on to produce work for *Roy of the Rovers*, *Judge Dredd,* and *Doctor Who*. However, none of these mean as much to him as *The Adventures of McFly and their Magic Bus*.

WARWICK JOHNSON–CADWELL
1976

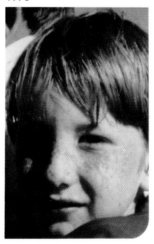

Warwick Johnson–Cadwell lives in Portsmouth with his wife and three children. He has been drawing stories as long as he can remember, through school, university and alongside all his day jobs (which do, occasionally, include professional illustration). Encouraged by a tide of enthusiasm from the comics community after posting work on his blog, Warwick began making comics. During the last couple of years his work has appeared in the anthologies:

Birdsong, *New British Comics*, *Solipsistic Pop* and *West*. He has also recently drawn *Tag Team Tastic* for *The Dandy*. He is currently working on *Gungle*, and another book, *Hunch Parsons*, both to be published in 2012 by Blank Slate.
www.warwickjohnsoncadwell.blogspot.com

LUKE PEARSON
1976

Luke Pearson is an illustrator and comic book artist based in Tamworth. He graduated with an illustration degree in 2010. His comics can be found in anthologies such as *Paper Science*, *Solipsistic Pop* and *A Graphic Cosmogony*, music newspaper *The Stool Pigeon*, the self-published *Dull Ache* and scattered across the Internet. He was also the main artist on Channel 4's educational game *The End*.
Luke is the author of *Hildafolk* and *Everything We Miss*, both published by Nobrow Press.
www.lukepearson.com

PAUL HARRISON–DAVIES
1977

Paul Harrison–Davies started reading comics in the 1970s, and never stopped. Sometime in the 1990s he decided to make his own, starting with the self published, *Fun Comics, featuring The Big 3*, which lasted six issues. Paul is also a contributor to *BAM*, several AccentUK anthologies, *Best New Manga* volumes 1 and 3, *Toxic*, and Boom's *Zombie Tales*.
www.paulhd.blogspot.com

KATIE GREEN
1978

Katie Green is a freelance illustrator based in Bristol. She has a degree in biology, and another in sequential illustration. She also bakes a wicked vegan cake. Katie self-publishes a bimonthly zine, *The Green Bean*, and other limited-edition projects. She is currently working on her first graphic novel, *Lighter Than My Shadow*, to be published by Jonathan Cape in 2013.
www.katiegreen.co.uk
www.katiegreenbean.blogspot.com

PAUL PEART–SMITH
1979

London-based Artist/Writer Paul Peart-Smith lives with costume designer Yolanda and together they spawned an ever-growing monster named Jet. And they've all been adopted by Minxy the cat. Paul has been drawing for the last 21 years, and couldn't imagine life any other way. His first published work, *Slaughter-*

bowl, appeared in *2000AD*. He has created character designs for clients such as The Jim Henson Workshop and Sony Entertainment. Comics, however, have an unnatural hold on his soul. Together with colleague, George Nelson, Paul has recently curated an exhibition focused on black comics and creators, entitled *Black Power.*
www.poboi68.wordpress.com
www.comicspace.com/poboi

GLYN DILLON
1980

Glyn Dillon lives in London. He was born in 1971, the youngest in a family where all the men are artists. His wide-ranging career has included: comic books, illustration, storyboarding for both film and television, and a short period of directing music video promos. Glyn has worked as a concept designer for both films and toys. He is currently writing and illustrating his first graphic novel, *The Nao of Brown*, for SelfMadeHero.
www.naobrown.com

I.N.J. CULBARD
1980

I. N. J. Culbard lives in Nottingham. He started out as an animation director, directing com-

mercials, developing TV shows and producing and directing short films. He was first published in 2006 as part of Dark Horse Comics' *New Recruits* anthology. He has appeared in *Dark Horse Presents, Judge Dredd Megazine, 2000AD* and has drawn several graphic novels for SelfMadeHero with writer Ian Edginton, including: *The Picture of Dorian Gray, The Hound of the Baskervilles, A Study in Scarlet, The Sign of the Four,* and *The Valley of Fear.* Recently, he has adapted and drawn H. P. Lovecraft's *At the Mountains of Madness.*
I.N.J. Culbard is currently adapting and drawing H. P. Lovecraft's *The Case of Charles Dexter Ward* and Edgar Rice Burroughs' *A Princess of Mars*, to be published by SelfMadeHero in 2012.
www.strangeplanetstories.blogspot.com

JOHN ALLISON
1981

Self-taught artist and miser John Allison lives in Manchester. He accidentally became one of the first webcomic artists in 1998, with his daily strip *Bobbins*. He rose to prominence in 2002 with *Scary Go Round*, an Internet phenomenon which ran for seven years. During this time, he designed a lot of t-shirts that people really liked, and a few that people just didn't understand at all.
Despite giving away almost everything he has ever drawn for free online, John has earned a living for eight years this way. His current project is called *Bad Machinery* and it's about mystery solving children. John is the author of *Peloton, Ahoy Hoy, Ghosts, Heavy Metal Hearts and Flowers, Girl Spy, Recklessly Yours, Retribution Index, Looks Brains and Everything* and *Giant Days.*
www.scarygoround.com
www.badmachinery.com

PHILIP BOND
1982

Born in 1960s Lancashire, Philip Bond now lives in New York, married to his DC editor and producing infrequent, but well-loved comics for both DC and Marvel. While Philip may have married into US mainstream comics, he'd like to believe he's still indie at heart. Philip started his career in Worthing's seminal comics scene, writing and drawing *Wired World* for *Deadline* magazine from 1988 to 1993. After working at *2000AD*, he went on to draw books for DC, including: *Kill Your Boyfriend, The Invisibles, Vertigo Pop: London,* and *Vimanarama,* all for DC's Vertigo imprint.
www.philipbond.net
www.flickr.com/photos/planetbond

D'ISRAELI
1983

Matt Brooker lives in Nottingham, and wishes he had a cat. Under the pen name D'Israeli, he has been a comic artist since 1988. As an early adopter of digital media, he has produced all his work on computer since 1999. Matt is a regular contributor to *2000AD,* for whom he has drawn *Judge Dredd.* Other career highlights include *Lazarus Churchyard* with writer Warren Ellis, *Timulo* for Deadline magazine, and inking on the groundbreaking *Sandman* series. He is perhaps best known for his collaborations with

writer Ian Edginton, which include: *Kingdom of the Wicked, The War of the Worlds, Scarlet Traces,* and *Leviathan,* published by Dark Horse Books, and *Stickleback,* published by 2000AD Books.
He has recently drawn *SVK,* an experimental comic written by Warren Ellis, printed in two colours plus a special ink only visible under ultra violet light. *SVK* is published by BERG London.
www.disraeli-demon.blogspot.com
www.getsvk.com

SIMONE LIA
1984

Simone Lia is an artist living and working in London. Her better-known comic characters include a chip, a bean and a bunny in denial. Her strips have been published in the *Guardian* and The *Independent* and her comic artwork has recently been exhibited at The Tate Britain. Simone is the author of the graphic novel *Fluffy* published by Jonathan Cape. Currently, she is working on a new book about a woman, a hermit, a horseman and a husband.
www.simonelia.com

DARRYL CUNNINGHAM
1984

Darryl Cunningham lives in Yorkshire. His long stint working as a health care assistant on an acute psychiatric ward was the inspiration for his book *Psychiatric Tales,* published by Blank Slate in the UK, and Bloomsbury in the US. He

is currently working on *Uncle Bob Adventures*, and a second volume of *Psychiatric Tales,* also for Blank Slate. *Science Stories*, a book debunking scientific naysayers and conspiracy theorists, will be published by Myriad Editions in 2012.
www.darryl-cunningham.blogspot.com

JONATHAN EDWARDS
1985

Jonathan Edwards lives in Wales, where he collaborates with his partner, Louise (AKA Felt Mistress), to create bespoke fabric creatures. His illustrations appear on record sleeves for bands, including the Black Eyed Peas and the Jungle Brothers, and weekly in the *Guardian* newspaper. Jonathan's comics first appeared in *Deadline* and *Tank Girl* magazine back in the mid-1990s. Since then, he's contributed to a Belle and Sebastian-themed anthology for Image Comics, and drawn *A Bag of Anteaters*, written by Ian Carney and published by SLG. He is the author of *Aunt Connie and the Plague of Beards*, published by Les Cartoonists Dangeroux. Jonathan has recently written and drawn a weekly strip, *Pop,* for the NME.
www.jonathan-e.blogspot.com
www.jonathan-e.com

ADE SALMON
1986

Born in Blackpool, Ade Salmon studied illustration at Manchester Polytechnic. He graduated with a First and went on to produce a wide range of illustrations for magazines, advertising and publishers, including: Panini, Titan, and Rebellion. In 1993, he broke into the British comics industry, working simultaneously at *Doctor Who Magazine* and *Judge Dredd Megazine*. He has drawn *The Cybermen, Dr Who, Judge Karyn, Rugrats, Cosmic Adventures*, various Marvel superheroes, and covers for Big Finish's *Bernice Summerfield*.
Ade was Chief Colourist for *Dr Who Magazine* and *Dr Who Adventures* comic strip for over two years. Exhausted from colouring other artists' work, he worked with American Writer/ Director Robert Tinnell to create *The Faceless: A Terry Sharp Story* graphic novel for Image Comics. Returning to the worlds of Dr Who, he drew strips for *Torchwood* magazine, American publisher IDW's *Dr Who* comic, and most recently, *Forever Dreaming* in *Dr Who Magazine*. Next, he'll be drawing a Lovecraft adaption for SelfMadeHero.
www.adriansalmonart.blogspot.com

KATE CHARLESWORTH
1987

Kate Charlesworth was born in Barnsley, studied graphics in Manchester, freelanced in London and now lives and works in Leith, Edinburgh. Her work has appeared in editorial, advertising, publishing, TV animation and electronic media. She exhibited at the Shrewsbury International Cartoon Festival in 2010.
Kate's vast printed output includes: comics for Fanny Publications, a long-running strip for *New Scientist* magazine called *Life, the Universe and (Almost) Everything*, the books *The Cartoon History of Time* (with John Gribbin) published by Abacus, and *All That – the Other Half of History* (with Marsaili Cameron), published by HarperCollins.
www.katecharlesworth.com

WARREN PLEECE
1988

Warren Pleece lives in Brighton. He has worked in comics for over 20 years, beginning by self-publishing the dark, sarcastic magazine *Velocity* in the late-1980s with his brother Gary. During the last few years he has worked mostly for DC Comics' Vertigo, drawing the well-received graphic novels *Incognegro* for DC Vertigo and *Life Sucks*, for First Second Books. An anthology of early work, *The Great Unwashed*, is forthcoming from Escape Books.
Warren is the author of the graphic novel *Montague Terrace*, published by Jonathan Cape.
www.activatecomix.com/73.comic
www.warrenpleece.wordpress.com

KRISTYNA BACZYNSKI
1989

Kristyna Baczynski is an illustrator, comic book artist and designer of Yorkshire tongue and Ukrainian blood. She likes new pens and old paper. She draws, screenprints and animates creatures, cartoons and comics that come from somewhere between the Pennines, the Carpathians and the gutter. Her animated short, *Java Jive*, won the 2008 Northern Design Award. Her sequential work has been published in *Solipsistic Pop, Paper Science* and *NibLit*.
www.kriskicorp.blogspot.com

HARVEY JAMES
1989

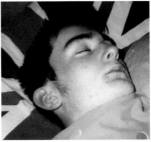

Harvey James is a comic artist and designer from Stafford. He came to comic books having designed for video games and TV. Currently, he's working on a series of short stories. He believes the golden age of comics is right now. His recently completed book, *A Long Day of Mr James Teacher*, is now available through Blank Slate's Chalk Marks imprint. His next, *Zygote*, is published in 2012.
www.harveyjamestm.com

RIAN HUGHES
1990

Rian Hughes lives in Ealing. He collaborated on the 1990s *Dan Dare* revamp for *Crisis* magazine with writer Grant Morrison and several series for *2000AD*, including: *Tales from Beyond Science* with writer Mark Millar, and *Robo-Hunter* with writer Peter Hogan. He is an award-winning graphic designer and typographer who has produced designs for watches, CDs, animated films and Hawaiian shirts for clients from Tokyo to New York. A collection of his comic strip work, *Yesterday's Tomorrows*, is published by Knockabout Comics.
www.devicefonts.co.uk

SEAN PHILLIPS
1991

Sean Phillips lives in the Lake District with his wife and three sons. Drawing comics professionally since the age of fifteen, Eisner Award winning Sean has worked for all the major comics publishers, including: 2000AD, Marvel, DC and Dark Horse. Since drawing *Sleeper*, *Hellblazer*, *Batman*, *X-Men*, *Marvel Zombies*, and Stephen King's *The Dark Tower*, he has concentrated on creator-owned books, including: *Criminal*, published by Titan Books, *Incognito*, published by Marvel and *Seven Psychopaths*, published by Delcourt. Sean is now working on a sequel to the recently optioned *Incognito*, while also drawing another book for Delcourt.
www.seanphillips.co.uk

PETE DOREE
1991

Pete Doree's partnership with Sean Phillips goes back to early childhood, when they produced *The Kids of Rec Road*, a strip in which their twelve-year-old selves had adventures with every major Marvel character. He produced the humour strips *Get In the Ring* for Classic Rock magazine and *The Infernal Gods of Electric Disaster* for Guitarist magazine, and self-published, *Essential Showcase Presents: Stan & Jack*. With Sean Phillips, he's written the western "The Brothers MacKenzie" for Image's

Outlaw Territory Vol. 2 and 1930's adventure *Gabe & The Sandpiper* for Dark Horse Presents. Pete is currently writing about how great 1970s comics were on his website.
www.bronzeageofblogs.blogspot.com

KATE BROWN
1992

Kate Brown lives and works making comics alongside her partner, fellow comic-book artist Paul Duffield, in Oxford. She frequently visits schools and libraries to host workshops about making comics. She has worked with SelfMadeHero, Accent UK, FactorFiction, Robinson, Barron's, ILEX, Hasbro and the *Guardian*. Kate is the author of *The Spider Moon*, published by Random House and originally serialised weekly in *The DFC*. *The Spider Moon* was adapted into a theatrical work by Playbox Theatre in late 2009, and was nominated for the 2010 Northern Graphic Novel Award. In January 2010, Kate was awarded the Arts Foundation Graphic Novel Fellowship. She used the funding to create her most recent work, *Fish + Chocolate*, published by SelfMadeHero.
www.danse-macabre.nu

SIMON GANE
1992

Cartoonist and illustrator Simon Gane lives and works in Bristol. His first published comics ap-

peared in punk fanzines in the early 1990s. Recent projects include: the graphic novels *Paris* (with Andi Watson), for *SLG*; *Dark Rain: A New Orleans Story* (with Mat Johnson); and *Northlanders* (with Brian Wood), for DC/Vertigo; and illustrations for the *Gym Shorts* children's books published by Roaring Brook Press.
www.simongane.blogspot.com

JON McNAUGHT
1993

Jon McNaught is a printmaker and cartoonist living in Bristol. He also works as a printmaking instructor at the University of the West of England. He has produced comic strips for *Nobrow, Art Review* and *Stripburger,* among others. His first book *Birchfield Close* was published in 2010 by Nobrow Press, as was his second, *Pebble Island.* He is working on another book with Nobrow for release in 2012.
www.jonmcnaught.co.uk

ADAM CADWELL
1994

Adam Cadwell works as a freelance artist and lives in Manchester, UK. He is the creator of the webcomics *Blood Blokes* and *The Everyday.* Adam has also contributed work to the anthology *Solipsistic Pop,* and to *Phonogram,* published by Image Comics.
www.adamcadwell.com

FAZ CHOUDHURY
1995

Faz Choudhury lives in North London. His early work was published in the comics anthologies *Scenes From the Inside* and *Le Roquet.* He was a member of the Les Cartoonistes Dangereux comics collective, for which he wrote and drew *The Malice Family* book. Faz has also inked various Panini UK titles, including *Doctor Who Magazine,* and provided illustrations for *Horrible Histories* and *Horrible Science.* His most recent comics work was *The Elephant of Surprise* for Solipsistic Pop and the children's strip, *Dead Pets Society,* for *The DFC* and the *Guardian.* He has also made facial hairpieces for theatre, TV and film.
www.fazchoudhury.blogspot.com

JAKe
1996

Born in Hull, JAKe lives in East London. After working for *NME, Esquire* and *Time Out,* his designs for The Prodigy on their *Fat of the Land* recording brought him international attention. He has designed toys, animation and illustration, working with Sony Playstation, *The Times,* the *Guardian,* the BBC, Channel 4, Sci-Fi Channel, Disney, XL Recordings, Ministry of Sound, Fatboy Slim, Ugly Duckling, Prince Fatty and Steinski/Sugarhill Records, as well as collaborating with The Mighty Boosh, Carhartt,

Colette/Comme Des Garcon and the t-shirt labels 2K by Gingham and Gimme 5. JAKe has a longstanding relationship with Lucasfilm, and his *Star Wars* artwork has appeared on merchandise worldwide, from Adidas sneakers to a t-shirt worn by George Lucas himself.

He has recently illustrated *How to Speak Wookiee* for Chronicle Books and the graphic novel *Hellraisers* for SelfMadeHero.

www.jake-art.com
www.designtaxi.com/jake
www.jakestarwars.com

JEREMY DAY
1996

Jeremy Day, formerly Jeremy Dennis, lives in Oxford with her husband and two cats. She stumbled into the UK comics scene in the early 1990s, wielding a variety of photocopied comics and went on to make many, many more, culminating in her long-running series *Three in a Bed*. Jeremy's strips have appeared in many comics anthologies with rude names, including: *Dykes Delight, Girlfrenzy, Lezzie Smut, Whores of Mensa* and Roberta Gregory's *Naughty Bits*. For the last ten years she has mostly been grappling on the Internet with the inappropriately named project *The Weekly Strip*.

www.jeremyday.org.uk

DAN MCDAID
1997

Dan McDaid was born and raised in Cornwall. He has designed video games, worked on a venerable women's magazine, taken third place in an online comic artist contest and drawn twelve issues of the ill-received series *Jersey Gods* with writer Glen Brunswick for Image Comics. After contributing illustrations to the *Doctor Who Storybook,* Dan went on to both write and draw for *Doctor Who Magazine* in the UK and the US. He collaborated with writer Steve Horton on a *Bizarro* story for DC Comics' *Superman 80-Page Giant 2011*. He is currently working on titles for Oni Press.

A collection of his Doctor Who material, *Doctor Who: The Crimson Hand* is published by Panini Books.

www.danmcdaid.blogspot.com

ROGER LANGRIDGE
1998

Roger Langridge was born and raised in New Zealand. He moved to the UK in 1993, and lives in London with his wife Sylvie, their two children, and a box of his own hair. He has been producing comics for over twenty years. Most recently, he attracted critical attention for his work on the Harvey-Award winning *Muppet Show Comic Book* published by Boom! Studios. His *Thor: The Mighty Avenger* series, with artist Chris Samnee is available in two collected volumes from Marvel Comics. Other works of note include: Marvel's *Fin Fang Four*, Fantagraphics' *Zoot!* and *Art d'Ecco* (in collaboration with his brother Andrew). Roger is currently writing and drawing *Snarked!*, an ongoing series that takes the characters of Lewis Carroll off in new and unexpected directions. *Snarked!* is published by Kaboom!

He is the author of *Fred the Clown*, nominated for *Ignatz, Eisner, Harvey* and *National Cartoonists' Society* awards.

www.hotelfred.com

WILL MORRIS
1999

Will Morris lives and works in London. He self-published his first comic *The Cotton Fox* in 2010 for a friend's charity pop-up shop. Rediscovering the joy of drawing and finding the fantastically supportive UK comics community was enough to convince him to throw aside six grueling years of office work in favour of studying for a Master's degree in Illustration.

Will is currently working on a new comic *The Silver Darlings*, set in the autumn years of the Scottish herring fishing industry, for Blank Slate's Chalk Marks imprint.

www.whmorris.blogspot.com

DAVE SHELTON
2000

Dave Shelton was born and raised just outside of Leicester. He now lives in Cambridge, which suits him pretty well. Dave likes the music of Tom Waits, the films of Billy Wilder and the books of P. G. Wodehouse. He also likes tea, cake, cricket and talking about pens.

He is the creator of the comic noir children's strip *Good Dog, Bad Dog* which appeared in the *Guardian*, *The DFC*, and in a collection published by David Fickling Books. He hopes to complete the second volume of *Good Dog,*

Bad Dog sometime later this century.

www.daveshelton.com
www.daveshelton.blogspot.com

CAROL SWAIN
2000

Born in 1962, in London, Carol Swain was raised in rural Wales. She studied painting at art school and began her comics work by self-publishing *Way Out Strips*. She is the author of two graphic novels, *Invasion of the Mind Sappers* and *Foodboy*, more recently, she illustrated her partner Bruce Paley's autobiographical book *Giraffes In My Hair*; all published by Fantagraphics. An anthology of her stories, *Crossing the Empty Quarter*, was published in 2009 by Dark Horse. Carol is currently working on a third graphic novel called *Gast*.

HUNT EMERSON
2001

Hunt Emerson lives in Birmingham. He has drawn cartoons and comic strips since the early 1970s. His work appears regularly in publications as diverse as the *Beano*, *Fiesta*, and *Fortean Times*, and he has contributed to countless other magazines and comics. His comic strips have been translated into ten languages, and he has been awarded several comic strip prizes. In 2000 he was named as one of the 75 Masters of European Comics by the CNBDI, the French comics academy.

Hunt has written around 30 comic books and albums, mainly published by Knockabout Comics. These include: *Lady Chatterley's Lover, Casanova's Last Stand, The Rime of the Ancient Mariner, Thunderdogs, PussPuss, CityMouth, Aliens Ate My Trousers,* and *The Festival Ritual.*

DUNCAN FEGREDO
2002

Duncan Fegredo has been drawing comics professionally since 1988. Highlights include: several collaborations with writer Peter Milligan, notably, *Enigma, Girl,* and *Face* (currently in development as a motion picture), all published by Vertigo (DC Comics). Also of note is a collaboration with Writer/Director Kevin Smith, *Jay & Silent Bob: Chasing Dogma,* published by Oni Press.

Currently, Duncan is drawing *Hellboy: The Fury* for Creator/Writer/Artist Mike Mignola, the closing chapter of a larger story comprising *Darkness Calls, The Wild Hunt* and *The Storm & The Fury.* Hellboy is published by Dark Horse Comics.

www.beautysonlyasliceaway.com

PHILIPPA RICE
2003

Philippa Rice lives in London. Since 2008, she has been making people feel sentimental towards recyclable materials with her webcomic *My Cardboard Life.* Philippa's Internet shopping addiction and habit of looking through bins has provided plenty of cardboard and paper supplies for making five new collage–comic strips every week. She is the artist behind *Intricate Dwellings* and is a contributor to *Solipsistic Pop 3* and *Paper Science.*
www.mycardboardlife.com

JOSCELINE FENTON
2004

Josceline Fenton lives in London. She is a third-year graphic design student at the London College of Communication, specialising in design for print and illustration. Her first self-published comic was called *Circle,* and for the last year she has been producing a weekly webcomic called *Hemlock.* The first and second chapters are now collected in print as *Hemlock#1* and *Hemlock#2.*
www.hemlock.smackjeeves.com

GAREN EWING
2004

Garen Ewing lives in West Sussex. He was born in 1969, started school in 1973, and left England in 1985 to live in California for a year. On his return, he attended art college but dropped out after six months. He found work as a mushroom farm porter and forklift driver, hotel porter, newspaper layout artist, multimedia

developer, graphic designer, and self-employed illustrator and writer. He's half Scottish, one-sixteenth Romany Gypsy, a karate black belt, and an expert on the Second Anglo-Afghan War of 1878–1880. He is the creator of *The Rainbow Orchid: Adventures of Julius Chancer*, published by Egmont.
www.garenewing.com

TOM HUMBERSTONE
2005

Tom Humberstone lives and works in London. He is an Eagle-Award winning creator and the editor and publisher of UK comics anthology *Solipsistic Pop*.
His comics include: *My Fellow Americans, How to Date a Girl in Ten Days, Art School Scum,* and *Everything You Never Wanted to Know About Crohns Disease*.
www.tomhumberstone.com

DAN BERRY
2006

Dan Berry resides quietly in Shrewsbury from where he runs *The Comics Bureau* website. He is a senior lecturer at the North Wales School of Art & Design, where he leads the specialism in graphic novels. He is the author of *Oxford Clay, Silky Wilson, Onion Soup, Shoulder to Shoulder with Pavlov* and *Lasagna*.
www.thecomicsbureau.co.uk
www.thingsbydan.co.uk
www.oxfordclay.com

ALICE DUKE
2007

Alice Duke is an illustrator, currently based in Liverpool. She does drawings, paintings and comics for books, videogames and films.
www.aliceduke.com
www.alicedraws.blogspot.com

POSY SIMMONDS
2008

Posy Simmonds lives in London. She started her first daily strip *Bear* in The *Sun* in 1969, and also contributed to publications including *The Times* and *Cosmopolitan*. After moving to the *Guardian* she created *Mrs Weber's Diary*, a popular cartoon strip about middle-class couple George and Wendy Weber. She was named 'Cartoonist of the Year' in 1980 and 1981.
In the late 1990s, her serial *Gemma Bovery* appeared weekly in the *Guardian* and was published as a book in 1999. She then wrote and drew *Literary Life* from November 2002 until December 2004. Her most recent *Guardian* series, *Tamara Drewe*, was published as a book in 2007. In 2010, the story was adapted into a feature film. Posy was made a Member of the Order of the British Empire in 2002 for

her services to the newspaper industry. In 2007, she illustrated the opening titles of the BBC's production of Elizabeth Gaskell's *Cranford*. After being nominated in 2001 for *Gemma Bovery*, Posy won the 2009 *Prix de la critique*, awarded by the Association des Critiques et des Journalistes de Bande Dessinée for *Tamara Drewe*. Her children's books include *Fred*, *Lulu and the Flying Babies* and *Baker Cat*. The many collections of her *Guardian* strips, including *Literary Life*, and her graphic novels *True Love*, *Gemma Bovery* and *Tamara Drewe* are all published by Cape.

LAURA HOWELL
2008

Laura Howell lives in Birmingham. She has been a professional comic artist since 2006, and a compulsive scribbler for her entire life. She is the first female artist to work for the *Beano* in its 73-year history, and is also a regular contributor to *Toxic*, *Mad Magazine* and *Viz*. Her comic strip work includes: *Johnny Bean from Happy Bunny Green*, *Meebo & Zuky*, *Ratz*, *Les Pretend* and *Minnie the Minx* for the Beano, *The Mighty M* and *Sneaky: The Cleverest Elephant in the World* for *The DFC*, *Robin Hoodie*, and her award-winning *The Bizarre Adventures of Gilbert & Sullivan*.
www.laurahowell.co.uk

ANDI WATSON
2009

Andi Watson lives in Worcester with his wife and daughter, and scribbles on bits of paper at the kitchen table. He grew up reading stories lying on the living room floor and scribbling on pieces of paper. He ended up telling his own stories in a variety of styles and genres. His *Skeleton Key* series has been collected in several volumes, and his graphic novels include: the sublime *Paris*, drawn by Simon Gane, *Love Fights*, *Slow News Day*, *Breakfast After Noon* and *Little Star*, all published by SLG.

Andi is the author of *Glister*, a series of books for children published by Walker Books including: *The House Hunt*, *The Haunted Teapot*, *The Family Tree*, and *The Faerie Host*. His new series for children, *Gum Girl*, is published by Walker books in 2012.
www.andiwatson.biz
www.flickr.com/photos/andiwatson

DAVE TAYLOR
2010

Dave Taylor lives and works in Liverpool. After many failed attempts at being a rock star he drew comics for Marvel UK and then Marvel US. He went on to work for DC Comics on various *Batman* titles for many years until a dispute with editors culminated in his retirement from comics. After a period of illness he came out of retirement to work on *Judge Dredd* and *Judge Anderson* for *2000AD* to great acclaim.

Dave is co-creator of the *Tongue*Lash* series, written by Randy and Jean-Marc Lofficier, published in English by Dark Horse, and six other languages. He has recently completed a new *Batman* 'prestige-format' book for DC Comics to be published in 2012.
www.davetaylorart.blogspot.com/

ACKNOWLEDGMENTS

Cover designed by Woodrow Phoenix
Cover art by Rob Davis

Pages 62–66
Colours by Rob Davis
Pages 96–100
Written by Rob Davis
Pages 183–187
Colours by Geraint Ford
Pages 223–226
Written by Woodrow Phoenix

Thanks to:

Paul Gravett
Peter Stanbury
Corinne Pearlman
Alison Sampson
Faz Choudhury
Andrew Salmond and Josh Palmano at GOSH!,
London
Clark Burscough and Lisa Wood at
Thought Bubble, Leeds
Mike Allwood and Phil Davis at the Bristol
International Comic Expo
Ben Cornish, John Nicholls,
and Bill Schanes at Diamond
Amy Gilbey and Rebecca Burgess at Shelter
Anita O'Brien at The Cartoon Museum
Claire Thompson at Turnaround Publisher
Services
Oliver East
Kate Evans
Duncan Bullimore

Special thanks to Rachael Karadayi for driving
me crazy and keeping me sane. *R D*

Thank you, Bridget Hannigan for your inspired
'Leap Year' idea, for pep, persistence and for
expertly proofing and copy-editing this beast.
You rock! Kisses, *W P*

Without the always-on microblogging network
which connects the UK comics community
together in a constant stream of Tweets, this
project might never have happened.
Thank you, Twitter.

mrphoenix
@Robgog Why, thank you. So how long do we have to
wait before you reveal yr collaborative idea?
23 Nov at 15:28

Robgog
Use the exquisite corpse form to tell one man's life story
1968 - present- 1st artist does 1 day in '68, next one
continues with 1 day in 69
23 Nov at 15:37

mrphoenix
I've never heard of this being done. Do it, would be XLNT!
23 Nov at 15:38

Robgog
end up with 'A life', long as each creator is faithful to what
precedes to some degree could be quite wonderful.
23 Nov at 15:40

mrphoenix
Sounds good. Maybe keep it to 3 pages each.
23 Nov at 15:42

Robgog
Yeh, I'd like people to have some leeway though.
23 Nov at 15:45

Robgog
something 'genetic' about the idea of creating someone's
life story like this.
23 Nov at 15:46

mrphoenix
You're right. Up to 5 is best. Each one a fragment of the
helix!
23 Nov at 15:51

Bl

3

Contents

Introduction

GOOD IDEAS just float about you all the time. Sometimes you grab one and call it your own, but owning it means nothing unless you do something with it. On Tuesday, November 23 last year, I stopped for lunch and my thoughts wandered around like a band of drunks. I'd not long returned from Thought Bubble, a comics festival in Leeds, where I was inspired by the industry and imagination of the creators and the quality of the books and comics on show. The UK comics scene seemed alive in a way I had not seen before. Or ever expected to see. So many different men and women of all ages and backgrounds coming at the same medium from so many different angles. This most definitely wasn't just a collection of boys with their superhero comics under their arms queuing for autographs. I discussed with a few people I met there the idea of getting as many as possible of these UK talents into a kind of "Best of British" anthology, and I was thinking about this as I ate.

Then the idea for Nelson floated past, fully formed, and I grabbed it. I announced on Twitter that I was now in the possession of a brilliant idea and, given how busy I was with other projects, was quite happy to leave it at that. But people wanted to know what it was, and Woodrow Phoenix, in particular, embraced it as soon as I explained it to him.

What was the idea? It was quite simple really. We would take a single life from birth (in 1968, the year I was born) up to the present day and give each comic creator a single day from each year, to create a life story from snapshots. I was inspired by the notion of a host of creative people, whose work I loved, coming together to create not just a story but a complete person. With every story being done year-by-year, the novel would grow out of the storytelling instincts of all these creators. Of course, a game of consequences is fun to watch and to be part of, but the game element wasn't key in the vision Woodrow and I had for this book. Above all, we wanted to create a novel. As editors, we were determined to keep a close eye on the evolving story for consistency and vision, helping everyone to rise to the challenge as we occasionally steered the ship away from the rocks. We asked that people trusted their instincts and we, in turn, trusted our own.

I think we've succeeded. Fifty-four people have created a single story, pulling from their own lives, their experience as storytellers and their skills as image-makers. I don't know that any other medium could pull this off. This book is a testament to what comics truly are, and to the fact that people who make comics do it out of love of this form. Read on.

ROB DAVIS

PAUL GRIST

SATURDAY, JUNE 15 1968.

JOY OF A TOY

COME ON IN KIDS

I'M LOOKING FOR A TOY — A TOY MODEL OF LORD NELSON.

LORD HORATIO NELSON? VICE ADMIRAL OF THE FLEET? FIRST DUKE OF BRONTE?

KENNEDY DEAD AGAIN!

A STANDARD ONE T' THIRTY SCALE COMPOSITE MINIATURE?

THAT'S THE LITTLE ONES IS IT? I DON'T WANT A LITTLE TOY SOLDIER.

I WANT ONE THAT'S ABOUT A FOOT HIGH.

JoOOoaN! LAD 'ERE SAYS HE WANTS A FOOT HIGH MODEL OF VICE-ADMIRAL NELSON — WE GOT ANYTHING LIKE THAT UP THERE?

NELSON?

I HAD ONE WHEN I WAS A KID, WEIGHED A TON! MADE O' LEAD I SUPPOSE. ME MUM USED TO USE IT AS A DOOR STOP... HIS HEAD USED TO COME OFF IF YOU PULLED IT.

OOF. CAREFUL. DON'T WANNA BE CALLING IN SICK TOMORROW!

RIGHT, THERE'S THE LEGS ON NOW. PLUG IT IN, GET THE FELLA TUNED IN... BOB'S YOUR UNCLE!

HEH HEH, NOW LOOK AT THAT! MAN, JUST LOOK AT THOSE TWO LITTLE FACES, EH? LIKE TWO PEAS IN A POD! HEH HEH!

YOU KNOW WHAT -- IT'S FUNNY. I DON'T REMEMBER YOU EVER SAYING THAT YOU HAD A BOY TOO.

NO. WELL... YES. WELL... WE DIDN'T HAVE HIM LONG.

THE TWINS WERE A BIG SURPRISE, I CAN TELL YA. WE HAD AN INSTANT NUCLEAR FAMILY! I WAS SO HAPPY I DIDN'T KNOW WHAT TO DO WITH MYSELF.

WE ONLY PLANNED ON ONE. WE HAD THE NAME AND EVERYTHING. WE WERE GOING TO CALL HIM NELSON.

THEY WERE SO BEAUTIFUL I COULD HARDLY BELIEVE IT.

HOW FINISHED THEY WERE. LIKE TWO SIDES OF THE SAME COIN.

SO IN THE END WE CALLED HER NEL AND HIM SONNY.

SHE WAS PERFECT. LOOK AT HER. WE THOUGHT HE WAS, TOO. BUT WE SOON FOUND OUT.

POOR LITTLE FELLA WAS IN TROUBLE FROM THE OFF. HE HAD A HOLE IN HIS HEART.

FIVE MONTHS, THAT'S ALL WE HAD WITH HIM.

FIVE MONTHS AND THEN HE WAS GONE.

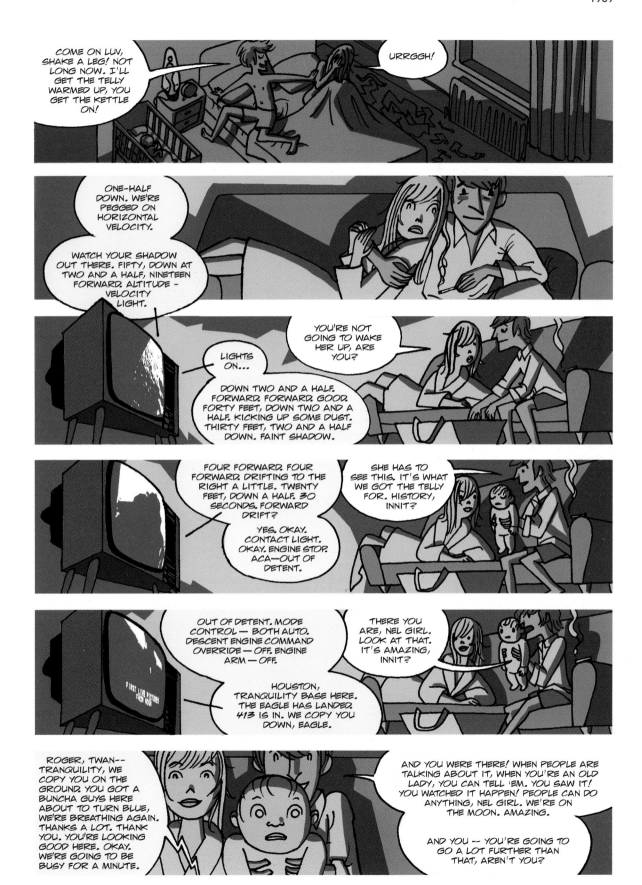

Rita, love, they'll sort you right out.

Come see my man—he's BRILLIANT.

For a while after the little one died, the doctor put me on some PILLS.

I don't know, sweets, but you've been so low...

Maybe your sister's right?

It was Beeba's idea—she's very MODERN, a pill for everything.

The pills were strange. They kept me from focusing my sadness... If I tried to see my little boy's hands, his face... it was like a photograph what weren't developed right.

I was BLURRED.

That's her tenth time 'round, today, easy.

Lass looks all MIXED UP, poor thing.

Sorry, Nel...

Mummy's a bit...

WHAA!

But I didn't need to FORGET... I needed to GRIEVE.

After a while I only took two a day... then ONE... I think the first thing I noticed, when I came out of the fog, was Jim noticing ME. The smile on his face, when he realized I was back... that was it...

WHAT?! What is it?

PUFF PUFF

Nothin', sweets.

Just nice to see you smile.

That made quitting worth it.

But goin' it without that fake sunshine glowin' down on me... that was tough.
I think the worst moment was when Nel turned one. I was so angry—not at Nel, bless 'er, she's a lovely, contented little soul. Just a blind, speechless rage—at having gotten a glimpse of the family I wanted... and then having it DIE, with my boy.

Where IS that girl?!?

Rita, honey, it's time to cut the cake!

KAY KAY!

Don't cry... don't cry...

But by then.... I knew myself... I knew what I needed...

WELL it's about time! Where've y~

Marlene, can I have a word?

Of course!

KOO!

Mrs. B, how 'bout you do the honours?

For a moment, I froze. How could I say what I was going through?

What's wrong, Rita?

It's just...

It's just...

And then I said that word, the one I'd tried not to say... not even at home... no, I was too afraid, for so long, of my heart, and his, just falling to pieces.

Sonny.

Some'd say havin' a cry at your baby girl's party's selfish.

I know, honey.

I still think about mine, too.

I say, walk a mile in my shoes— and then PISS OFF.

COMICS EH? DO YOU WANT ONE? CHOOSE WHATEVER YOU LIKE.

CAN I HAVE THIS ONE?

UM.. SURE! WHY DON'T YOU CHOOSE YOURSELF A LOLLY TOO..

IT'LL COOL YOU DOWN.

SSHLP

I DON'T LIKE THE SUN MARLENE.

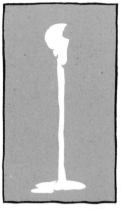

THE GIRLS ARE FINE. THEY WANT TO KNOW HOW SHE IS. AND HOW YOU ARE.

OH IT'S ALRIGHT, ERROL CAN LOOK AFTER DEZZIE FOR ONE NIGHT.

I'M SO GLAD TO HEAR SHE'S OKAY..

SATURDAY, JUNE 25 1977

Psssst!

Sniff!

BRMVM!

poot!

zzzzzz!

Monday, April 24 1978

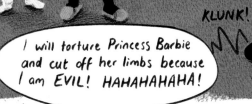

AAAAAAAAH-HA-HA-HA-HA!!!!

BAM!

BA-BAM!

WHAT'S THE MATTER? WORRIED YOU'RE MISSING BLUE PETER?

LEAVE HIM ALONE, ASHLEY!

BA-BAM!

BAM!

ONE FOR ALL AND ALL FOR ONE, REMEMBER?

NOBODY GETS TO TELL US TO STOP RUNNING OR TO BE QUIET. THE SCHOOL IS OURS!

YESSSSS!!

COME ON!!

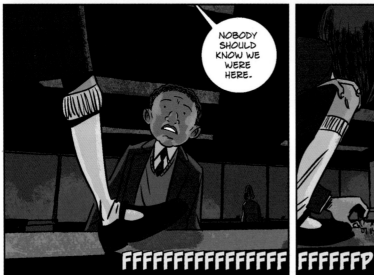

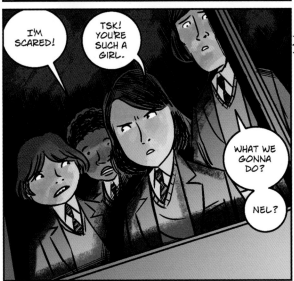

FRIDAY, AUGUST 13 1982

TOYAH
BELOVED
GOLDFISH
1981-
1982

THREE DAYS AFTER THE RUSSIANS DROPPED THE BOMB. DAGENHAM IS A CHARRED, IRRADIATED CRATER.

ME, TABITHA AND LES ARE HOLED UP IN DAD'S FALLOUT SHELTER AT THE BOTTOM OF THE GARDEN.

DAD GOT THIS 'PROTECT AND SURVIVE' MANUAL AT THE POST OFFICE. OUR KEY TO SURVIVING THE NUCLEAR WINTER.

"STOCK ENOUGH FOOD FOR 14 DAYS. FOODS WHICH CAN BE EATEN COLD... TINNED, OR WELL WRAPPED. CEREAL, BISCUITS, MEAT AND VEG..."

CRISPS, FIZZY POP.

MM! PICKLED ONION FLAVOUR!

LES! THAT'S SUPPOSED TO LAST US 14 DAYS!

THOSE AT THE EPICENTER WILL BE VAPOURISED INSTANTLY! FURTHER FROM THE BLAST- BURNED ALIVE!

THEY MAY BE THE LUCKY ONES. AT THIS DISTANCE WE ARE SHOWERED WITH RADIOACTIVE FALLOUT. ANYONE EXPOSED WILL BE TRANSFORMED INTO HIDEOUS MUTANTS!

MUM, DAD. ALICE... POOR ALICE.

SO YOUNG. SO MUCH TO LIVE FOR.

WILL SHE BE A MUTANT NOW?!

PROBABLY, YES. HAIRLESS AND DROOLING, KILLING TO SURVIVE.

RIGHT. I'M STARTING ON THE BEANS THEN. I'LL NEED THE ENERGY TO FIGHT OFF THE MUTANT HORDE.

57 BAKED BEANS

LESLIE, IF YOU WERE THE LAST MAN ON EARTH, AND ME AND NEL WERE THE LAST TWO GIRLS...

WHICH OF US WOULD YOU CHOOSE AS YOUR MATE?

SO. THE MANUAL SAYS WE SHOULD CHECK FOR RADIO TRANSMISSIONS. THERE MAY BE INSTRUCTIONS FOR SURVIVORS...

♫ ...NO DON'T SAY A PRAYER FOR ME NOOOOW... ♫

ACE! DURAN DURAN!

TUESDAY, SEPTEMBER 27 1983

PUBLIC RECREATION GROUND

BASTARDS!

STINKING BUNCH OF BASTARD *TOSSERS!*

UH. 'LO, NEL.

"YOU CAN'T WASTE YOUR WHOLE BLOODY LIFE SCRIBBLING," SHE SAYS! *SCRIBBLING!*

OH, EXCUSE ME FOR BEING GOOD AT SOMETHING.

I, UM –

BLOODY PARENTS EVENING – "YOU COULD BE DOING SO MUCH BETTER AT *MATHS*, NEL,"

'IF YOU DO THE *SPECIAL HELP* SESSIONS WE MIGHT EVEN GET YOU INTO THE *'O' LEVEL* GROUP, HOW WOULD THAT BE?'

ER, WHAT?

CHRIST, AREN'T YOU *LISTENING?* THEY WANT ME TO JOIN THE DIVVY SET FOR EXTRA CATCH-UP CLASSES IN MATHS AND WHEN IS DIVVY MATHS? *FRIDAY AFTERNOON* –

HALFWAY THROUGH BLOODY ART. *THE ONLY BLOODY THING IN THAT BLOODY SCHOOL I GIVE A BLOODY SHIT ABOUT, LESLIE.*

OH.

YES. *OH.*

THEY SAY I'LL HAVE NO TROUBLE CATCHING UP IF THEY CUT MY ART LESSONS THIS YEAR. WELL, THANK YOU VERY MUCH, SEVEN KINGS, THANK YOU FOR RUINING MY LIFE. AGAIN.

JUST HAD A *MASSIVE* ROW WITH ME MUM ABOUT IT.

YOU AN' YOUR MUM, ALWAYS ROWIN' THOUGH, AREN'TCHA?

OH, NOT LIKE THIS. *NEVER* SEEN HER LIKE THIS.

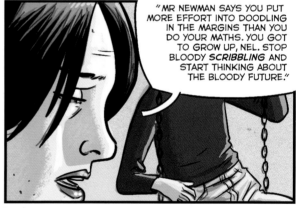

"MR NEWMAN SAYS YOU PUT MORE EFFORT INTO DOODLING IN THE MARGINS THAN YOU DO YOUR MATHS. YOU GOT TO GROW UP, NEL. STOP BLOODY *SCRIBBLING* AND START THINKING ABOUT THE BLOODY FUTURE."

THEN DAD PIPES UP LIKE THE VOICE OF DOOM, "IT'S ALL GETTING *TORN DOWN*, THE FACTORIES, THE SHIPYARDS, IT'LL BE THE *MINES* NEXT – THERE WON'T BE ANY FUTURES FOR YOUR GENERATION THAT'S WHY YOU NEED YOUR EDUCATION."

I CAN'T BLOODY WIN – THEY WANT ME TO THINK ABOUT MY FUTURE AND THEN TELL ME THERE *IS* NO BLOODY FUTURE! SO WHAT'S THERE TO AIM FOR? BEST-QUALIFIED GIRL IN THE *DOLE QUEUE?*

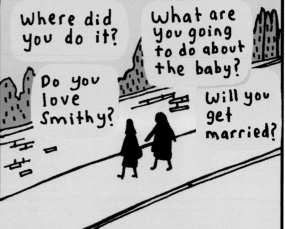

FRIDAY, SEPTEMBER 21 1984.

MY VERY FIRST DIARY ENTRY. 1984 MAY NOT BE TOO MUCH LIKE ORWELL'S POLICE STATE, BUT THERE ARE ECHOES OF IT IN MRS THATCHER'S SUPPRESSION OF THE MINERS' STRIKE.

TODAY I SAW LESLIE IN THE STREET.

COAL NOT DOLE

SOCIALIST WORKER!

HEY NELLIEPHANT!

HEARD ABOUT THE OLD SCHOOL? IT NEARLY BURNT DOWN.

SOMEONE SET FIRE TO A CLASSROOM IN THE MIDDLE OF THE NIGHT. NOTHING TO DO WITH YOUR FREAKY, FOUR-EYED FRIEND, WAS IT?

YOU USED TO BE NICE, LESLIE. WHAT HAPPENED TO YOU?

YOU HAPPENED TO ME, NELLIEPHANT. YOU DID.

YOU'LL LIVE.

I SUPPOSE I'LL HAVE TO.

DAD IS WINDING ME UP.

WHAT'S THAT MUSIC BLASTING OUT OF YOUR ROOM?

PRINCE.

PRINCE, EH? HE'S THAT HALF PINT WHO THINKS HE'S HENDRIX. YOU OUGHT TO LISTEN TO SOME PROPER MUSIC, LIKE LED ZEPPELIN.

THAT'S THE SORT OF MUSIC YOU LISTEN TO NOW YOU'RE AT ART COLLEGE, IS IT?

I'M GOING OUT.

WHY DOES DAD KEEP WINDING ME UP? HE'S CHANGED SINCE HE WAS MADE UNEMPLOYED.

I MET UP WITH TABITHA IN THE PARK. SHE'D USED THE DOG AS AN EXCUSE TO GET OUT OF THE HOUSE. WE COMPARED DADS.

YOUR DAD SEEMS LIKE A GOOD BLOKE TO ME.

OH YEAH?

I'D SWAP MY DAD FOR YOUR DAD, ANY DAY. I WANTED TO GET CONTACT LENSES, BUT HE WON'T LET ME.

HE THINKS CONTACT LENSES ARE VAIN. VANITY IS ONE OF SATAN'S TRAPS, ACCORDING TO THE ELDERS.

I'VE KNOWN TABITHA FOR FOUR YEARS, BUT ONLY RECENTLY HAS SHE BEGUN TO BE MORE OPEN ABOUT HER FAMILY.

NO BIRTHDAYS IN MY FAMILY. NO CHRISTMAS. NO FUN AT ALL. YOU'RE LUCKY I'M ALLOWED TO BE FRIENDS WITH YOU.

WITNESS FAMILIES DON'T USUALLY MIX WITH NON-CHURCH PEOPLE.

THE CHURCH THINKS THE OUTSIDE WORLD IS RUN BY SATAN.

HEY, WHAT HAPPENED TO YOUR HAND?

OH, I BURNED IT.

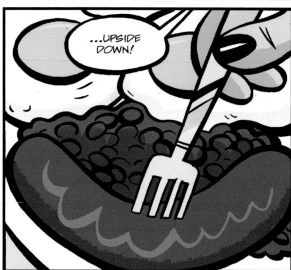

I'M WORRIED IT'S LOOKING A BIT TOO "CARTOONY" IN PLACES. TRY NOT TO GO DOWN THAT ROUTE, NEL MY DEAR.

ALSO – A BLACK LINE NEVER WORKS WITH COLOUR.

BUT EGON SCH

EGON SCHIELE! WHAT ON EARTH WOULD ART STUDENTS DO WITHOUT EGON SCHIELE? NEVER MIND, CARRY ON!

IGNORE THE OLD SOD.

BILLY BRAGG

HE'S NEVER BEEN RIGHT SINCE BEARDS WENT OUT OF FASHION.

I LIKE IT. IT'S NICE TO USE YOUR MEMORIES..

...RATHER THAN JUST ERASE THEM.. LIKE POOR OLD DURAN DURAN.

SORRY, THAT'S RUDE.

I HAVEN'T EVEN INTRODUCED MYSELF, HAVE I?

I'M CHRISTIAN. PLEASED TO MEET YOU?

CHRISTIAN, MY LITTLE TORY FRIEND, I'M AFRAID THAT GIRL IS A LAW UNTO HERSELF.

HEY, NELSON!

HEH HEH!

I CAN'T FIND HER ANYWHERE...

THAT'S YOUR OWN FAULT FOR HAVING SUCH A BIG HOUSE!

AH, LOOK, IT'S TABS! BUT WAIT... THE INVITE SAID FANCY DRESS?!

HA FUCKIN' HA! WHAT DID YOU COME AS – AN ARSEHOLE?

I'M ELVIS!

I'M STEVIE WONDER!

COURSE, ELVIS WAS A SMITHS' FAN.

THIS PARTY'S LIKE THE END OF CIVILISATION – I'M GOING HOME.

THAT'S AN OXYMORON! YOU'RE HOMELESS, TABITHA!

I'VE GOT A PROPER HOME NOW, THANKS LES! I LIVE IN THE TOTTENHAM SQUAT WITH THE ANARCHIST COOKS!

WE LOOK AFTER EACH OTHER, MORE THAN I CAN SAY FOR THE REST OF HUMANITY!

I THOUGHT A JOINT BIRTHDAY PARTY FOR ME AND NEL WOULD BE A GOOD IDEA, BUT...

FOR A GUY WHO'S BEEN TRYING TO GET IN HER KNICKERS FOR A YEAR, YOU DON'T KNOW MUCH ABOUT NEL, DO YOU?

NEL *HATES* BIRTHDAYS! ESPECIALLY HER OWN.

HEY YOU! THE GIRL WITH HALF A NAME!

NEL!

RIGHT! WHO IS THAT? I'M WARNING YOU--!

WHY? WHAT YOU GONNA DO – EAT MY GOLDFISH?

WHO THE *FUCK* ARE YOU? YOU'RE NOT... YOU CAN'T BE!

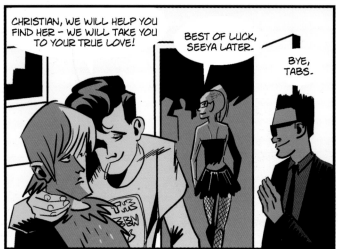

CHRISTIAN, WE WILL HELP YOU FIND HER – WE WILL TAKE YOU TO YOUR TRUE LOVE!

BEST OF LUCK, SEEYA LATER.

BYE, TABS.

HA! DEZZIE! YOU'RE THE LAST PERSON I EXPECTED!

REALLY? WHO DID YOU THINK IT WAS THEN?

THOUGHT YOU WERE A GHOST.

WHAT PART OF "PRODUCE A SET OF CHARCOAL STUDIES OF A LOCAL LANDMARK" DID YOU NOT UNDERSTAND, NEL?

WHA?!

WELL EVERYONE, WHAT DID WE ALL THINK OF NEL'S PERFORMANCE? DID IT HAVE ANY MERITS DESPITE HER COMPLETE MISUNDERSTANDING OF THE BRIEF?

WE'VE SEEN IT ALL BEFORE, HAVEN'T WE? YOUNG STUDENTS PLAYING AT BEING GROWN UP ARTISTS. I'M SURE I'M NOT THE ONLY ONE WHO FOUND IT EMBARRASSING? I MEAN, *MADCHESTER?!*

HMM, HMM. QUITE

ANYONE HERE THINK THE 'MADCHESTERS' WILL "CATCH ON"?

YOU DON'T *GET IT* DO YOU?! YOU ESPOUSE SO-CALLED ARTISTIC REVOLUTION AND THE MINUTE IT WACKS YOUR STUPID BEARDY FACE IN THE MOUTH *YOU CAN'T HANDLE IT!*

WELL, I'VE HAD ENOUGH OF THIS!

C'MON YOU LOT, ARE YOU COMING OR WHAT?

THE FUCKING TWATS! THEY TRY TO TEACH US TO BE INDIVIDUAL AND THE MINUTE WE SHOW SOME FUCKING INDIVIDUALITY, THEY *CAN'T FUCKIN'* *HACK IT!*

FUCKERS!!

I KNOW...

I MEAN, WHY CAN'T WE START A NEW MOVEMENT HERE IN MANCHESTER? THIS PLACE IS BUZZING WITH MUSIC AND CLUBS AND ART, AND...STUFF!

THE TUTORS ARE JUST JEALOUS, NEL. I MEAN, IF THEY WERE ANY GOOD, THEY WOULDN'T BE TEACHING US WOULD THEY?

WE WERE A BIT SHIT, THOUGH...

THOSE WHO CAN, *DO IT* AND THOSE THAT CAN'T, *TEACH!*

WE'LL BE THE ONE'S WHO *DO IT*- WE ARE THE *YOUTH*, WE ARE *MADCHESTERS*, WE ARE *UNITED*, WE ARE THE *FUTURE...*

AND WE ARE SHIT

SO WHAT? WE ARE SHIT AND WE DON'T *GIVE A FUCK!*

NOW, WHO'S WITH ME?

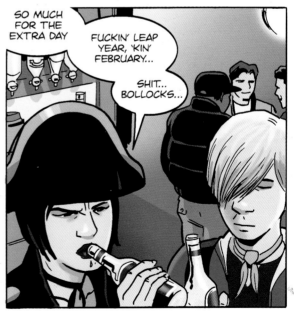

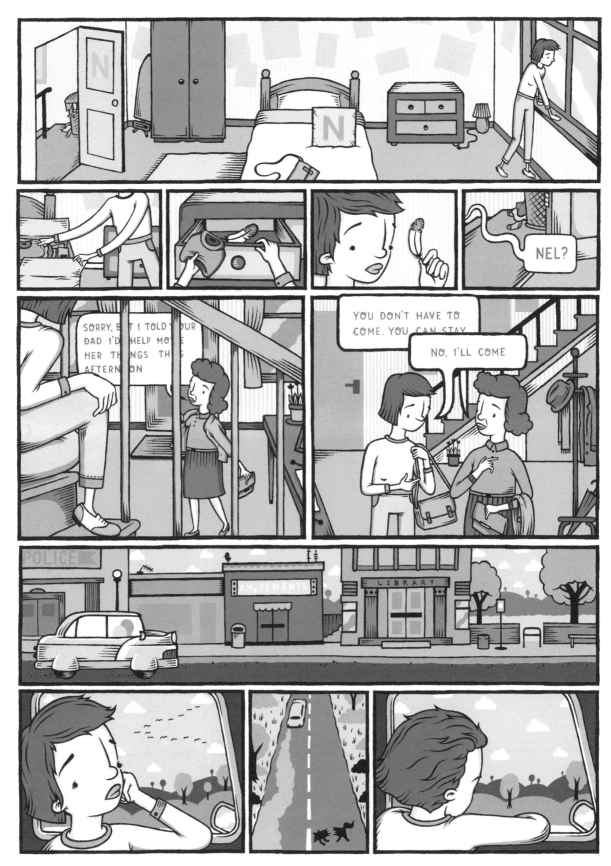

GOTTA GET THAT TEMPERATURE JUUST RIGHT...

I SAW DAD YESTERDAY.

WHAT? WHERE? DID YOU TALK TO HIM?

SATURDAY, JUNE 12 1991

HE'S OUR DAD, ALICE.

OH NEL, I DIDN'T MEAN THAT, AND YOU KNOW IT.

BUSTER! NO! NOW, YOU STAY AWAY FROM THERE!

HOW IS SHE SINCE THE DIVORCE?

OH, SHE'S FINE SO LONG AS SHE STAYS BUSY, Y'KNOW.

AND, OF COURSE, SHE'S GOT BUSTER.

YEH, I'M SURE HE'S A GREAT HELP, IF SHE EVER NEEDS A DRAUGHT EXCLUDER.

NOW WHY D'YOU HAVE TO DO THAT?

JUST TRYING TO LIGHTEN THE MOOD. SORRY FOR EXISTING.

I DON'T THINK I'D BE ABLE TO TALK TO DAD, Y'KNOW. NOT AFTER WHAT HE DID. AND AS FOR HER...

YEAH, WELL, YOU'RE NOT LIKELY TO RUN INTO EITHER OF 'EM AT WAITROSE, ARE YOU?

ANYWAY, CAN WE CHANGE THE SUBJECT?

OK, HOW'S WORK?

I HATE IT. OBVIOUSLY. BUT I MIGHT HAVE SOLD SOME ARTWORK TO...

MM. ISN'T IT ABOUT TIME YOU GAVE UP ALL THAT...?

NO, ACTUALLY, IT ISN'T. WHY? WHAT'CHU MEAN?

NEL, I DON'T MEAN THIS IN A BAD WAY, BUT... WELL, LOOK AT YOUR LIFE. LOOK AT MINE. I MEAN... I MEAN, DON'T YOU WANT WHAT I'VE GOT?

WHAT, GAVIN?!!

NOT GAVIN. I DON'T MEAN.... NO, ACTUALLY, I DO MEAN THAT. WHY NOT SOMEONE LIKE GAVIN?

BECAUSE...

DON'T YOU WANT A NICE HOUSE? MONEY IN THE BANK, ALL OF THAT?

'COURSE I DO, BUT ON MY OWN T...

OH NEL, YOU'RE NOT EIGHTEEN ANYMORE.

YEAH, WELL, I'M NOT SURE YOU EVER WERE.

I'LL OPEN ANOTHER BOTTLE.

OK.

SEE IF YOU CAN CHEER HER UP.

OK.

BUSTER! NO!

SPLAASH!!

THAT BAD BOY'S PUMPIN' OUT SOME SERIOUS HEAT NOW. SHOULDN'T BE MUCH LONGER.

FUNNY THE WAY LIFE GOES, INNIT?

MM

I MEAN, WHO KNOWS WHAT WOULD'VE HAPPENED IF YOU AND ME HAD MET FIRST...

WHAT?

ALICE, GOD BLESS 'ER, SHE WAS BORN TO BE A MUM, Y'KNOW WORRIMEAN?

BUT YOU, YOU'RE NOT LIKE THAT, ARE YOU?

SORRY, WHAT?

C'MON, NEL, ALL THOSE HIPPY SQUATS AN' THAT YOU USED TO... YOU'RE NOT TELLING ME YOU NEVER... Y'KNOW, MIXED IT UP A BIT?

FUCK OFF, GAVIN, AND WHILE YER AT IT, CUT THAT FUCKING PONY TAIL OFF. YOU LOOK LIKE THE TWAT YOU ARE.

WELL, NOW, WHAT ARE YOU TWO GABBING ABOUT?

KATE BROWN

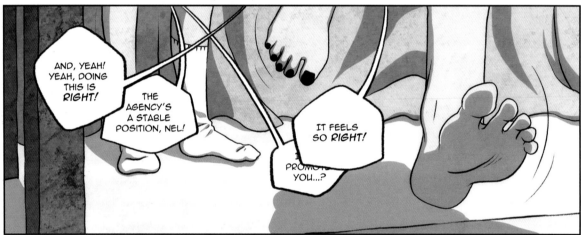

132

ADAM CADWELL

TUESDAY, MAY 10 1994

142

NEL!

TABS! OH MY GOD, IT'S GOOD TO SEE YOU!

YOU TOO!!! IT'S BEEN AGES!

OH NEL, THIS IS KAT MY LESBIAN LOVER

OH, HEY! NICE TO MEET YOU

YEAH, TABS HAS TOLD ME A LOT ABOUT YOU

SO, HOW ARE YOU? WHAT ARE YOU DOING IN THIS DUMP?

I'M... REVIEWIN' THE GIG FOR THE MAGAZINE

COOL! SO YOU'RE STILL AT 'THE FACE' THEN?

YEAH, I DO SOME MUSIC REVIEWS NOW AS WELL AS HELPIN' OUT WITH DESIGN. IT'S GREAT! UM... HOW'S UB GOING?

OH, REALLY GOOD, YEAH! WE HAVEN'T ACTUALLY MADE ONE IN A WHILE BUT LAST YEAR AT GLASTONBURY WE SOLD LIKE 150 COPIES!

THEN WE SPENT ALL THE CASH ON MAGIC BROWNIES! HA!

OH, WOW. THAT'S... GREAT!

SO... ARE YOU HERE FOR THE BAND? I DIDN'T THINK IT'D BE YOUR THING

IT'S NOT REALLY BUT KAT KNOWS THE SUPPORT BAND'S DRUMMER'S SISTER SO...

ALRIGHT, COOL. YOU SHOULD STICK AROUND THOUGH, THEY'RE AMAZIN'! THEY'VE BEEN GOIN' FOR YEARS BUT THEY'RE GETTIN' PRETTY BIG NOW

AND I LOVE THE SINGER! HE'S NOT AFRAID TO SOUND BRITISH Y'KNOW? I'M SICK OF ALL THESE BANDS JUST WANTIN' TO BE SONIC YOUTH OR THE PIXIES OR NIRVANA

OH, POOR KURT! I WAS A WRECK WHEN I HEARD. WHAT'S WRONG WITH NIRVANA ANYWAY?

NOTHING! I LOVE 'EM. I'M JUST EXCITED TO SEE BANDS DOIN' THEIR OWN THING. MUSIC IS GETTING EXCITIN' AGAIN LIKE IT WAS IN UNI

HA! WHAT WAS YOUR BAND CALLED? DO YOU STILL SING?

NO! HAHA. IT WASN'T A BAND IT WAS AN "ART PROJECT" AND I JUST SHOUTED STUFF

I THOUGHT YOU WERE GREAT!

SORRY I'VE BEEN SHIT AT KEEPIN' IN TOUCH

NO IT'S ALRIGHT. ME TOO. IT'S GOOD TO SEE YOU. YOU SEEM, I DUNNO, HAPPY

YEAH, I ACTUALLY LIKE MY JOB WHICH IS WEIRD AND MY LITTLE FLAT WHEN EVER I'M 'OME. I'M GETTIN' THERE Y'KNOW?

GETTING WHERE?

I MISS YOU NELSON

I MISS YOU TOO, TABBY

HI! SORRY I DIDN'T MEAN TO STARE

HEY, IT'S COOL I'M USED TO IT

NO, YOU REMINDED ME OF SOMEONE FOR A SECOND THERE

REALLY?

WHAT'S YOUR NAME?

IT'S FRANCIS

I'M NEL. PLEASED TO MEET YA

WILL YOU BE HERE LATER? I'VE GOT TO GO DO A THING

I'M 'ERE ALL NIGHT

CLAP CLAP WOOOOO

PLEASED TO MEET YA, TOO!

THIS. IS. AMAZING.

" AND YOU – YOU'RE GOING TO GO A LOT FURTHER, AREN'T YOU? "

WELCOME TO THE PLANET NELTRON. IT'S THE YEAR 3096.

<<Lazereye: current status: offline. Cellular reboot 89% complete.///

AND I NEED TWO FULLY FUNCTIONING PEEPERS TO TAKE THIS IN. I'M A CYCLOPS CYBORG, FASTER THAN A SPEEDING BULLET TRAIN, PULSING THROUGH THE VEINS OF THE GIANT ROBOT CITYDOME. THE BASSLINE STILL THROBS IN MY GUTS AND MY HEART HAMMERS A STEADY 135 BPM. I'M POWERED BY SAKE AND JETLAG. THE BEST COCKTAIL SINCE BRANDY AND BABYCHAM.

3096 AD, BUT THIS KNOBHEAD THINKS IT'S STILL 1966.

I'M FREEZING ME NUTS OFF. THOUGHT IT WAS GOING TO BE HOT. LAND OF THE RISING SUN MY ARSE. EH, YOSHI MATE, CAN WE GET SOME EGG AND CHIPS OR SUMMAT?

YEH, WELL I'M GLAD IT'S NOT HOT. I HATE THE BLOODY SUN.

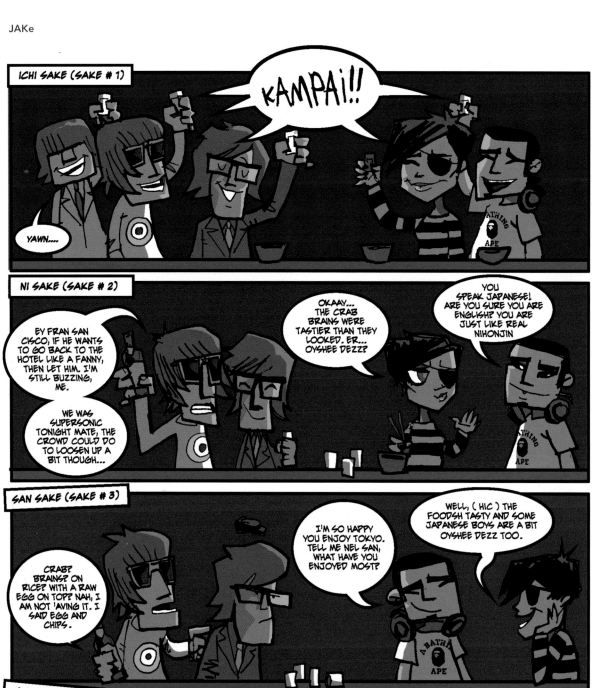

SUNDAY, AUGUST 24 1997

A BLACK HOLE, BIG ENOUGH TO FILL THE SKY. THAT'S IT, THAT'S WHAT'S HAPPENING NOW. YOU MIGHT LOOK UP AND SEE THE SUN, BUT NOT ME.

IT STARTED WITH THE SPICE GIRLS. ZIG-A-ZIG-AH. EVEN SOUNDS LIKE A MAGIC SPELL, DOESN'T IT? IF I HAD BEEN HERE I MIGHT HAVE BEEN ABLE TO DO SOMETHING ABOUT IT, BUT I WAS OUT OF THE COUNTRY AT THE TIME. ON TOUR, YOU MIGHT SAY.

JO WHILEY SAID THEY WERE LIKE THE BRITISH BEASTIE BOYS. SHE ACTUALLY *SAID* THAT, ON RADIO ONE. THAT'S WHEN I KNEW WE WERE FUCKED.

DON'T GET ME WRONG-- I LOVED THEM TOO. WE ALL DID. FIVE MANGA CHARACTERS COME TO LIFE, WHAT'S NOT TO LOVE? AND NOW LOOK.

FUCKING CTHULHU IS UPON US.

ANYWAY. MARLBOROS, PLEASE.

TEN OR TWENTY, LOVE?

FORTY.

Tuesday, June 16 1998.

YEAH... YEAH, IT'S OVER.

I WAS BEGINNING TO THINK DAD WOULD CLING ON FOREVER... BUT THEY'VE JUST LOWERED THE OLD SOD INTO THE HOLE. THE SOD INTO THE SOD! **HA!** SEE WHAT I DID THERE?

HOW'S THE TOUR?

OKAY. COOL. THANKS FOR CALLING, FRAN... KEEP IN TOUCH, YEAH?

ENJOY GERMANY.

HEY, NEL... YOU HOLDING UP ALL RIGHT?

UH. YEAH, I'M... UH...

ME NEITHER. I LIKED YOUR DAD. HE WAS REALLY NICE TO ME WHEN I USED TO COME ROUND.

TABBY...?

HELLO.

IS IT... IS IT **WRONG** THAT I'M STILL SO BLOODY **ANGRY** AT HIM?

WOULD IT HAVE **KILLED** HIM TO TELL THE TRUTH?

HIM? NO.

WOULD HAVE DEVASTATED **YOU,** THOUGH.

WHAT WOULD YOU RATHER HAVE -- A DAD WHO WAS HONEST AND FUCKED OFF, OR A DAD WHO LIED AND STUCK AROUND AND SUPPORTED YOU?

ME, I'D TAKE THE LIAR EVERY TIME.

ROGER LANGRIDGE

YOU WOULD REDUCE THIS MAN'S SACRIFICE TO A FOOTNOTE IN HISTORY?

CONTENT TO HAVE HIM BE REMEMBERED AS NAUGHT BUT A PIN-CUSHION.

NO MY FRIENDS! HIS BRAVERY HAS LENT US AN ADVANTAGE.

WE MUST LAUNCH A COUNTER-ATTACK ON THE FIENDS RESPONSIBLE.

AND IF WE WIN ONLY AN INCH OF TERRITORY...

...BY GOD IT'LL BE A GLORIOUS INCH!

YARRRRRGH!

WOW, NEL - THAT WAS AWESOME...

CHEERS MIKE.

THERE'S THE LAST OF THE BAD GUYS. WHERE'RE THE OTHERS?

NOT FAR BEHIND, BUT AT THIS RATE... NEL, WE MIGHT HAVE A NEW CHIEFTAIN.

WELL, MAKING AN IMPRESSION IS DEFINITELY SOMETHING YOU'VE GOT A TALENT FOR.

CHEERS MIKE, I'M ABOUT TO MAKE ANOTHER.

I'VE SPOTTED THE ENEMY CAPTAIN. I'M GONNA TAKE HIM OUT.

LORD AZGAROTH? YOU CAN'T! HE'S A 20TH LEVEL MAGE... YOU CAN'T!

MIKE, PERHAPS YOU'VE FORGOTTEN OUR BATTLE CRY:

"THOSE WHO CAN'T..."

"TEEEACH!"

ARRRGH!

WHUMMP!

MEN OF THE FOREST! THIS IS OUR DAY!

ANYONE?

WELL, SEE YOU ON MONDAY GUYS.

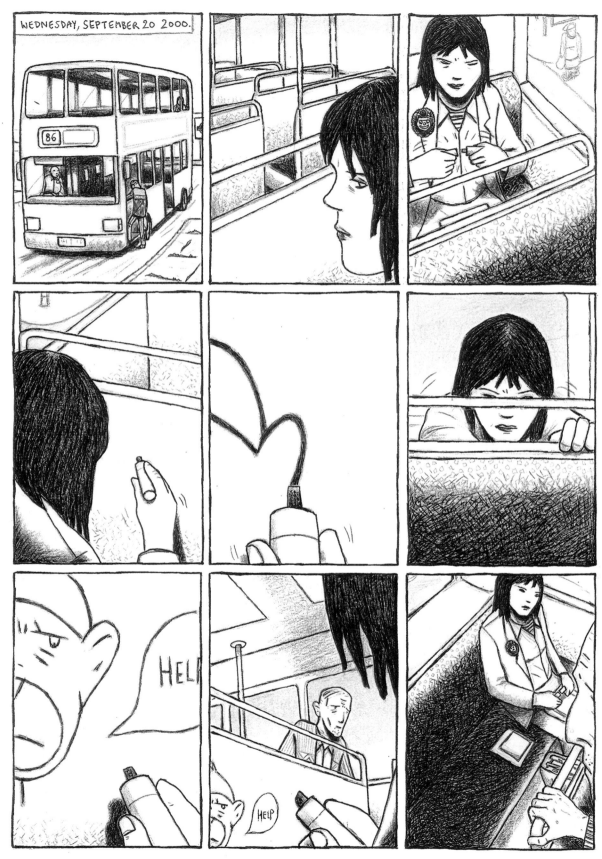

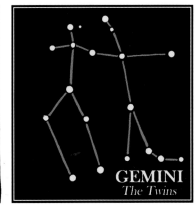

WHAT THE FUCK ARE YOU A TEACHER FOR, ANYWAY?

YOU HATED SCHOOL FROM DAY ONE!

AND THAT WAS BEFORE DAD AND MISS BUNTING...

...TOOK THE BAKER FAMILY OUT LIKE A HIJACKED 747.

IT WAS NEVER SUPPOSED TO BE THIS WAY. WE WERE SUPPOSED TO BE A TEAM. YOU AND ME AGAINST THE WORLD.

WAIT...

YOU LEFT ME, SONNY. LEFT ME TO DO ALL THIS ON MY OWN.

I'M SO TIRED... I CAN'T ...

GROUND ZERO.

SUNDAY, FEBRUARY 29 2004

WHY AM I EVEN PACKING HALF THESE CLOTHES? I CAN'T GET INTO THEM ANYMORE...

36 YEARS OF MY LIFE, ALL BOXED UP. FEELS BLOODY HIDEOUS.

I'D LIKE TO SEE YOU GET INTO THIS.

WHAT KIND OF PERSON KEEPS THEIR OLD SCHOOL UNIFORM?!

IT'S A PIECE OF MY LIFE! I'M NOT GOOD AT THROWING THINGS AWAY. ANYWAY YOU'RE JUST JEALOUS BECAUSE YOU NEVER WENT TO SCHOOL, TABS!

AHEM! I WAS WAY TOO COOL FOR SCHOOL!

YEAH, THAT'S WHY YOU USED TO BREAK INTO MY SCHOOL IN THE MIDDLE OF THE NIGHT, WASN'T IT?

FOR YOUR INFORMATION, I WAS NOT BREAKING INTO YOUR SCHOOL. I WAS BREAKING OUT OF MY HOUSE!

I KNOW, BABE. I KNOW.

I GUESS I WAS A BIT JEALOUS OF YOU OIKS AT SEVEN KINGS. I'D WATCH YOU ALL HAPPILY TROTTING PAST MY WINDOW IN YOUR BLAZERS AND TIES...

Take it again, scene three, from the top!

Squires Community Theatre, Reigate, Surrey.

Wednesday, September 15 2004.

"There you are, Mirabella! Lady Morton is asking for you!"

"Oh, Sable! I can't see her! She knows who took the gun! It was me!"

Excuse me, is one of you Mr Bolan, Charlie Bolan's father?

Uh-oh.

What? Yes? We're a little busy here, you know!

I believe this is yours?

Nora! Marvellous! Been looking for her everywhere!

Your son – hello, Charlie –

Hello, Miss Baker.

– brought this into school causing total chaos in my classroom.

I had children in hysterics, screaming ... complete mayhem!

How wonderful! Real theatre! Visceral! Alive!

Wait ...

Perfect!

If you could stand over here, just for a minute, maybe two!

I don't believe you're taking this seriously, Mr Bolan. This is a human skull! Now, Charlie's a bright kid ...

Great rehearsal tonight, really coming together. Thanks for standing in. Um, sorry about the, er ... *the scene...*

Oh no, no. That's all right. Difficult.

Yes, well. There it is. Into the jam, out of the jam, there'll always be jam, as dear old Nora used to say.

Um ...

So! How's my Charlie doing at school? Clever chap, isn't he, eh?

Well, Charlie, what do you think? How's school?

Okay.

Yes, Mr Bolan, Charlie's doing *okay*.

Marvellous! And you're his teacher, eh? What happened to Mrs... er, Mrs Hokum ...

Mrs *Hockham* left to have a baby. I've just moved down from London. New term, new place, new life ...

I see, I see. Well, this is us!

Just about pays the rent.

Very nice ...

BOLAN'S ANTIQUES

Oh!

Something interest you? You're welcome to come in ...

Er, no, no – thank you. I really should be getting home.

Goodnight, Miss Baker.

Goodnight, Charlie. See you at school tomorrow.

Not at all bad for a school teacher, eh? Almost human!

I like her.

Yeah ... yeah, me too.

COUGH!

OH THANK **CHRIST!!**

I'M OK... I'M OK!! THEY LET ME OUT

...

...

REALLY- I'M FINE

YOU'RE SHAKING

SO ARE YOU

I WAS WORRIED

ME TOO

SERIOUSLY- BACK IN LONDON LESS THAN A WEEK--

...

IS HE--

ALEX IS WITH HIM. HE'S FINE

DON'T THINK HE'S EVEN AWARE ANYTHING IS HAPPENING BEYOND THAT STAGE

HEH

LIKE FATHER...

...HE'S VERY FOND OF YOU NEL

Y'KNOW...

I KNEW YOU WERE NERVOUS ABOUT OPENING NIGHT

...BUT THERE WERE OTHER WAYS OF GETTING OUT OF IT...

HA HA HH HA HA HA HA HA
HA HA HA HA HA HA

...

...

NEL?

Friday, February 29 2008

No.

Definitely...no.

So, Facebook, who's up first? No contest!

Friendship confirmed.
You are now friends with Tabitha Colton.

Tabitha Colton
is smelling the coffee.

Employed at: Senior Consultant – Media Sector

Relationship status: In a relationship

Hometown: Stoke Newington

Tabitha has tagged you in a picture.

Ahh... so innocent back then.

View Tabitha's Albums

Nel Baker

Nel Baker

Nel Baker

Please, God, don't let any of my pupils' parents be on her Friends list.

Find friends

Francis Frearsl

Francis Frear
Networks: Mur

Francis Frears

Employed at: DJ @ At
Relationship status: Er
Hometown: Munich

Wow. She looks just like him.

Requests
You have 88 friend requests

Matt Forsythe	Confirm	Ignore
Mike Snook	Confirm	Ignore
Anna Madeley	Confirm	Ignore
Nina Porrit	Confirm	Ignore
Doug Bunting		
Kieron Lee		
Lina Gabrail		

Urgh, it'll take me forever to work my way through this lot...

Find frier

Desmond Hayne

A Friend request has been sent to Desmond Haynes.

Confirm Ignor

Confirm Ignor

What crazy stuff have *you* been up to, Force?

Confirm Ignor

Matt Forsythe
is taking his eldest swimming.
Updated 2 hours ago.

Employed at: Northern Rock

Hometown: Newport Pagnell

Relationship status: Married

View Photos of Matt (23)

Married with kids? Northern Rock? *Newport Pagnell?* No *way!*

▼ **Friends**

456 friends   See all

Dave White

Leslie Le Mezierre

Chad

Margaret

Jenny

Sigmund

And look who's on Matt's Friends list – Les Le Mez!

Yeesh, can't find any personal info amongst all these *apps.* Zombies, Vampires, Werewolves, Pokey Dokey, Causes, Sex Quizzes, Rate-My-Face, iLike, Butler Fight...

Still a twat, then.

Ashley Wright

Employed at: Barking and Dagenham Counc

Relationship status: In a relationship

Interested in: Men, friendship

Yoshi Ito

Employed at: Golden Gai

Networks: Tokyo

Relationship status: It's co

Christian Benedict Palmer-Ch

Christian Benedict Palme

Networks: University o

Relationship status: En
                                Bu

Hometown: Sevenoa

Scott Dunsheath

Employed at: BT (B

Relationship status:

Hometown: Birmin

Is there *anyone* out there who hasn't got a grown-up job and 2.4 kids?

Peter H

Peter H

How 'bout you, Fringe?

Peter Howitt
is having an early nigh
Updated 2 days ago

Employed at: Self-emp

Relationship status: Sir

Interested in: Women,

Birthday: December 1

YES! Single and balding!

Friendship confirmed.
You are now friends with Desmond Hayr

How do you know Desmond Haynes? [friend ▼]

Desmond Haynes
is watching CBeebies.
Updated 13 hours ago

Networks: London

Relationship status: Ma

Sex: Male

Hometown: London

Birthday: February 5 19

tos of Desmond (78)
mond's Albums

View Desmond's Albums

Lucky you, Desi. I bet Errol and Marlene are the best Grandparents *ever.*

Sonny Baker

Sonny Baker

Sonny Baker

You don't have a brother. Let it go.

So, you've finally been assimilated?

I may live to regret it. I've already been bitten by four vampires and asked to rank my top ten sexual positions.

And the *endless* baby photos! Look at it! It's like a massive *virtual fertility* contest.

Don't feel... left out, do you?

You know, it's not too late to change your mind. Plenty of women have babies in their forties.

Ben. Listen.

We've *thought* about it and *talked* about it and I'm surer than ever.

That primal, irresistible urge... I've never felt it. Well, maybe a *little*. But not *enough*.

It's not a club I need to join.

You'll just have to settle for *me*, then.

Settle?

I may be an *old fart,* but I still have all my own teeth, and I still have you and Charlie.

That's not settling, that's *WINNING.*

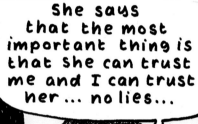

LET'S JUST TAKE IT ONE DAY AT A TIME. LISTEN, MY CALLING CREDIT IS UP. I'VE GOTTA GO.

YEAH, I'LL CALL YOU TOMORROW. I LOVE YOU TOO, BYE. BYE!

LAST WEEK WE WERE FLYING OUR DINNERS HALFWAY AROUND THE WORLD.

SUDDENLY IT'S NOT SUCH A SMALL WORLD ANYMORE.

IT COULD TAKE ME A MONTH TO GET HOME.

SUDDENLY I'M SO FAR AWAY FROM BEN AND CHARLIE AND EVERYONE ELSE I LOVE I MIGHT AS WELL BE ON THE MOON.

FOR A FEW YEARS WE FORGOT HOW BIG THE WORLD WAS AND HOW SMALL WE ARE.

MAYBE THIS IS HOW IT'S GOING TO BE FROM NOW ON.

BACK TO THE OLD, SLOW WAYS. STEAM. SAILS. HOT AIR BALLOONS.

NO MORE GLOBAL. JUST LOCAL.

EVERYONE CAN JUST STAY AT HOME FOR AWHILE.

MAYBE THIS IS WHAT THE PLANET NEEDS TO FIX ITSELF, TO PUT EVERYTHING BACK TOGETHER AGAIN.

WE'LL TELL CHARLIE'S CHILDREN ABOUT HOW WE USED TO TRAVEL HIGH ABOVE THE EARTH, HIGHER THAN ANY BIRDS COULD EVER GO.

IT WAS A MIRACLE AND WE WERE TOO CASUAL ABOUT IT FOR TOO LONG.

TUESDAY, JULY 19 2011

TRY LOOKING IN THE CUPBOARD ABOVE THE WASHING MACHINE...

WASHING MACHINE - YES! Y'KNOW THE BIG BOX WITH A ROUND WINDOW AND ALL THE SPINNING SOCKS INSIDE.

THAT'S THE ONES. PUSH AND TWIST...

WELL DONE, CHARLIE! YOU HAVE NOW SUCCESSFULLY CHANGED YOUR FIRST LIGHTBULB - THE WORLD IS YOUR OYSTER!

HA HA! OK, DARLIN', SEE YOU LATER ON. OH, AND AUNTY TABS SENDS HER LOVE.

I'LL TELL HER YOU SAID THAT!

I MISS LONDON. WELL, SORT OF. I PROBABLY GET THE BEST OF IT NOW. I MEAN LAST NIGHT WAS MAD FUN AND FRIDAY NIGHT WITH MUM ON THE MALIBU WAS SOMETHING ELSE ALTOGETHER!

I NEVER THINK OF YOUR MUM AS A DRINKER - SHE'S ONE OF THOSE PEOPLE WHO WERE JUST CREATED TO BE A MUM.

WELL, SHE USED TO BE A RIGHT GOER - FRIDAY NIGHT SHE WAS TELLING ME ABOUT HOW I WAS CONCEIVED IN A PUB! UNDER A BLOODY BILLIARD TABLE!!

OH, THAT IS CLASS!

NO WAIT. WAIT! THAT'S WHY YOUR DAD WANTED TO NAME YOU...

YEP, YOUR NAMESAKE IS IN THE BIBLE, MINE'S ON A PUB SIGN.

WHICH NELSON WAS IT?!? THERE'S ONE IN MERTON, ONE IN SHOREDITCH, ONE ON THE ISLE OF DOGS, ONE IN CAMDEN, ONE IN REGENT'S PARK...

THAT SOUNDS LIKE ME - ALL OVER THE PLACE.

OH, DO SHUT UP, NEL!

GIVE YOUR MUM A RING AND FIND OUT WHICH ONE IT WAS. OOH! WE SHOULD GO THERE FOR A PINT, PLENTY OF TIME BEFORE YOUR TRAIN.

WHY WOULD I WANNA DO THAT?